World of science

THE WORLD OF ANIMALS

BAY BOOKS LONDON & SYDNEY

1980 Published by Bay Books
157–167 Bayswater Road, Rushcutters
Bay NSW 2011 Australia
© 1980 Bay Books
National Library of Australia
Card Number and ISBN 0 85835 277 X
Design: Sackville Design Group
Printed by Tien Wah Press, Singapore.

THE KINDS OF ANIMALS

Living creatures can be divided into two main groups, plants and animals. They are usually easy to tell apart. Most animals can move about freely while plants are fixed in one place, although there are a few animals, such as anemones, which stay in one place, and some tiny plants, such as algae, which move about.

The very tiniest forms of life are called *micro-organisms* and can only be seen through a microscope. A large group of these forms of life is known as *Protozoa*, which means first animals. Even the largest protozoa, which are the *amoebae*, are no bigger than a pinhead. Their bodies are made of only one single cell. Probably these tiny, simple organisms are the ancestors of most other forms of living things. Some of their descendants have become animals, others plants.

If you have even a simple microscope, you can usually find protozoa in sea water, pond water or rainwater puddles. You can see them by examining a drop of water

One of the simplest forms of life, the single-celled amoeba continuously changes its shape as it pushes its cytoplasm out around the food that it absorbs into its body. Most amoebae live in water and reproduce by splitting into two separate cells: this is known as fission.

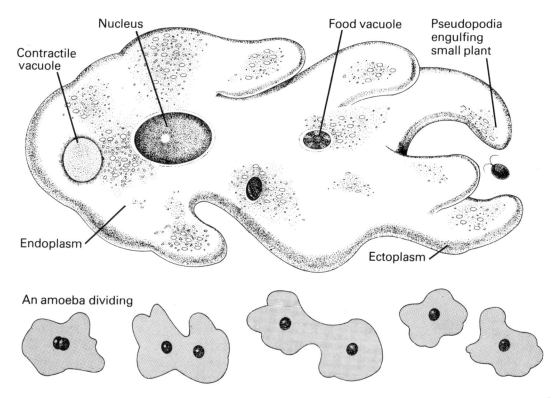

Nucleus

Food vacuole

Pseudopodia engulfing small plant

Contractile vacuole

Endoplasm

Ectoplasm

An amoeba dividing

Although they are both members of the **Metazoa** group, the blue whale, the largest animal ever, may weigh as much as 130 tonnes, whereas the minute rotifer varies from 0.1-2 mm in length. However, despite its size, the rotifer has a very complex multicellular structure.

from a tree trunk or a house drain, or by collecting a piece of seaweed in a jar; the sea water around it will contain protozoa. Some are fast swimmers, some are slow crawlers, others are fixed by stalks. All are interesting and some are beautiful to look at.

While the protozoa have only a single cell making up their body, the group called **Metazoa** have bodies made up of many cells. These animals range in size from the microscopic *rotifers* to the huge blue whale.

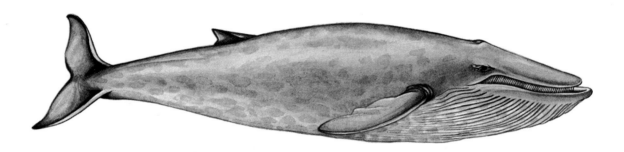

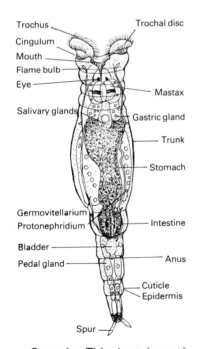

Trochus
Cingulum
Mouth
Flame bulb
Eye
Salivary glands
Germovitellarium
Protonephridium
Bladder
Pedal gland
Spur

Trochal disc
Mastax
Gastric gland
Trunk
Stomach
Intestine
Anus
Cuticle
Epidermis

Opposite: This chart shows the evolution of animals and plants from the first forms of life, which appeared on earth about 5000,000,000 years ago.

Species and genera

There are more than a million known kinds of animals and most of them are insects. It would be almost impossible to study them properly without classifying them in some convenient way, so they are arranged into groups so that any new organisms which are discovered can be placed in their correct group. All the members of each group are related to each other in some way.

An individual animal can always be described as belonging to a *species*. All members of a species are very similar and can breed among themselves to produce animals of the same kind. For example, a poodle and a great dane are both dogs and can interbreed though their offspring will probably be different in certain characteristics and size.

A Swedish naturalist called Carl Von Linnaeus invented the system of giving every species of animal a Latin name, made up of two words, so that scientists all over the world could understand the names. For instance, an American moose is called *Alces americana*.

Species which are very similar to each other are grouped together to form a *genus* (the plural is *genera*).

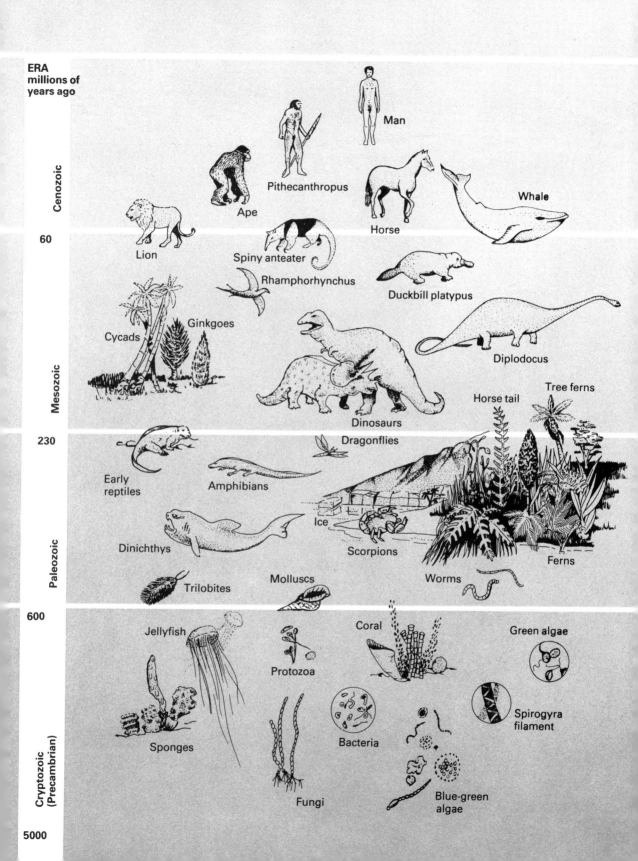

ERA
millions of
years ago

Cenozoic

Man

Pithecanthropus

Ape

Horse

Whale

Lion

Spiny anteater

Rhamphorhynchus

Duckbill platypus

60

Mesozoic

Cycads

Ginkgoes

Diplodocus

Horse tail

Tree ferns

Dinosaurs

230

Paleozoic

Early
reptiles

Amphibians

Dragonflies

Ice

Dinichthys

Scorpions

Ferns

Trilobites

Molluscs

Worms

600

Cryptozoic
(Precambrian)

Jellyfish

Protozoa

Coral

Green algae

Sponges

Bacteria

Spirogyra
filament

Fungi

Blue-green
algae

5000

So the first part of the Latin name tells us the name of the group or genus, while the second part of the name tells us something about the species. So *Alces americana* tells us that the moose is an American member of the genus called *Alces*, which includes all animals similar to the moose, such as reindeer.

Genera which have many similar features are grouped together in *families*. Families which have some things in common with other families are grouped into *orders* and the orders are grouped into *classes*, which form large groups containing many animals which seem different but which always share at least one characteristic.

Vertebrates and invertebrates

All insects, including this big onion fly, are invertebrates and have an external skeleton of chitin plates linked by very flexible muscles. Flies are found all over the world from the cold arctic regions to the humid tropics. Flies pass through four stages in their development: egg; larva; pupa; and finally the adult fly.

Two great divisions of the animal kingdom are those animals which have backbones, called *vertebrates*, and those which have no backbones, called *invertebrates*. Man is a vertebrate and so are most familiar animals such as dogs, cats and horses. Invertebrates include jellyfish and scorpions and worms. Most of the animals on earth are invertebrates, so there are more of these than anything else, but all the so-called *higher animals*, the mammals and the birds and reptiles, are vertebrates.

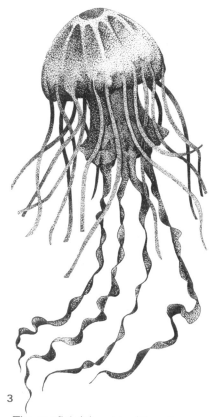

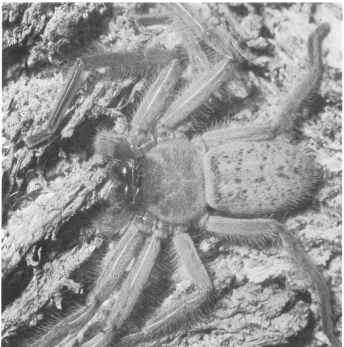

The starfish (1), spider (2) and jellyfish (3) are invertebrates. The vivid red starfish, or sea star, has five radiating arms and a supporting skeleton of calcite plates. The spider is often mistakenly labelled as an insect but is an arachnid. Its body is divided into two parts and it has four pairs of legs. Many jellyfish are dangerous to man and can cause severe rashes and stings. A mass of long tentacles hangs from the central umbrella-like jelly mass.

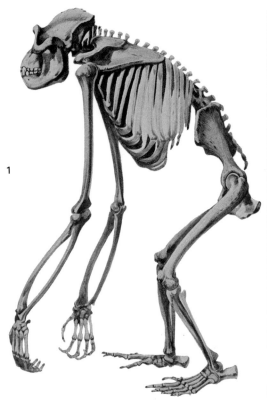

1

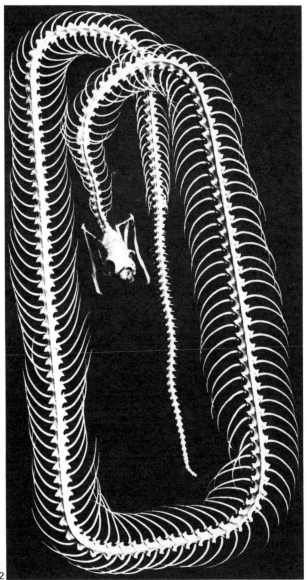

The skeletons of the gorilla (1),
snake (2) and blue whale (3),
like those of other vertebrates,
are called endoskeletons because
they are formed within the body.
Skeletons provide a framework
for the moving parts of the body
and protect delicate internal
organs. The skeletons of most
vertebrates are made of bone
and cartilage, which is partly,
composed of collagen.

2

3

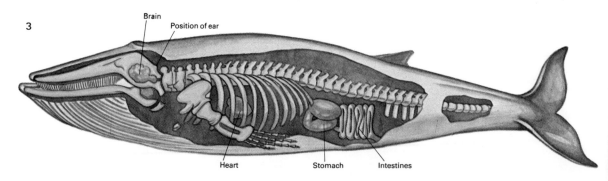

Brain

Position of ear

Heart   Stomach   Intestines

ANIMAL BEHAVIOUR

An animal's reactions to its surroundings can be called its *behaviour.* Seeking food and shelter, avoiding enemies and looking for a mate are all forms of behaviour. Most actions of an animal, such as freezing in one spot so it can hardly be seen when danger threatens, are done without the animal 'thinking' about them. The animal is able to perform such actions from the moment it is born and they are called *instinctive actions.* A fish can swim by instinct, although a child has to be taught.

Eating

Animals can be described according to their eating habits. As the name suggests a *herbivore* eats only plant material. The name is used to describe grazing and browsing animals such as rabbits, deer, antelope and cattle. Their cheek teeth are broad and well adapted for crushing and grinding plants and their stomachs and digestive systems are well suited to digest them. *Carnivores* are meat-eating animals. They include cats, dogs, foxes, wolves, weasels, lions and seals. The teeth of these animals are well adapted for their diet. They have large canine or eye-teeth

The Komodo dragon, a member of the monitor lizard family, is the largest species of lizard. Found on Komodo Island and some other Indonesian islands, the Komodo dragon eats smaller members of the same species and carrion. It sometimes will cannibalise other adults and has even been known to attack, kill and eat human beings.

This sambar deer, from southern Asia, is a herbivore. All deer are ruminants and have no cutting teeth or upper jaw incisors.

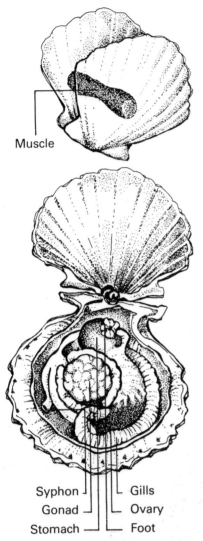

Muscle

Syphon ⌐ ⌐ Gills
Gonad ⌐ ⌐ Ovary
Stomach ⌐ ⌐ Foot

Bivalve molluscs filter their food from the water in which they live, picking up minute food particles with their long proboscides. Like Man, the badger is an omnivore and eats a mixture of plants and flesh. A member of the weasel family, the badger lives on fruit, fungi, cereals and small mammals.

for stabbing and tearing the food, and sharp-edged cheek teeth which slice the meat into small pieces. An animal which eats a mixture of plants and meat is called an *omnivore.* Man is an omnivore and so is the pig, bear and badger.

While most animals move about in search of their food, some water-dwelling creatures remain in one place and take particles they filter from the water. This group includes sponges, corals, anemones and familiar shelled animals like barnacles and mussels.

8

Food chains

Every living organism is involved in a food chain. For example, a snail eats leaves, a bird eats the snail, a cat eats the bird. Every food chain begins with some kind of plant as is shown by choosing any animal and following back the steps in its food chain. This is because plants are the only organisms which can make food by photosynthesis, in the presence of sunlight; so all animals are dependent on plants. Food chains are also known as *energy chains*, because it is through the various links in the chain that animals and human beings get their energy.

In a food chain, the sun's energy (1) is used by plants to make food. The plants (2) are eaten by herbivores, which, in turn, are eaten by carnivores (3). Both plant and animal substances decompose when they die (4) and return mineral substances to the soil where bacteria use them to provide carbon dioxide gas (5).

Sun

Defence

Almost all animals have some enemies. When one animal attacks another for food, the animal that is attacked is called the *prey,* the one that attacks is the *predator.* Most animals have ways of defending themselves and these ways are called *defence mechanisms.* One of the best known defence mechanisms is that of the skunk, which squirts a strong smelling liquid at its enemies. The liquid is formed in *glands* in the body.

Wasps and some other insects have stings which they use to inject poison into an attacker. Many stinging insects are brightly coloured. The bright colours are also a kind of defence mechanism because birds and other animals soon learn the bright colours mean something unpleasant and they leave the insects alone.

Hedgehogs and spiny anteaters or *echidnas* are protected by their prickly coats. When they are attacked, they roll up into a ball so that only the spines are showing. Some fish have a similar type of defence in the form of prickly scales on their bodies.

One of the most interesting defence mechanisms is that used by electric fish. These fish have special groups of muscles which can produce electricity and give electric shocks to other creatures that come too near. Some electric fish use this power to stun other fish for food.

While these creatures can all actually harm their attackers, there are many creatures that bluff by pretending to be larger or fiercer than they really are. The Australian frilled lizard frightens its enemies by spreading out a fold of skin around its neck like a frill. Many moths have large spots like eyes on their wings so that predators believe they are seeing the eyes of larger animals.

The conspicuous wasp uses its bright colouring and sting as a means of defence (3). Its sting is a modified form of ovipositor, which it injects into its victim and then withdraws, thus leaving a mixture of histamine and poisons in the victim. The Australian spiny anteater (2) has long, sharp spines and curls into a prickly ball to protect itself from predators. The skunk (1) raises its tail and arches its body in an intimidation display. It can squirt a foul-smelling liquid, which causes skin irritations.

1

2

3

Mimicry and camouflage

Mimicry is a kind of deception where the animal pretends to be something else. Many harmless creatures defend themselves by looking fierce and poisonous. True mimicry is a natural process by which the harmless creature takes on the same or very similar colouring and actions as a dangerous creature. In the insect world, most bees and wasps have stings and hairy bodies that are not pleasant for their attackers to eat. Other beetles, moths and flies escape being eaten because they look like the stinging creatures, although they really have no stings or other defences. Sometimes mimicry is used to help a creature obtain food. The praying mantis blends with the leaves and flowers of a plant. When insects come to the leaf-like mantis they are caught and eaten.

Camouflage is similar to mimicry, but the camouflaged creature is hiding in its surroundings while the mimic uses its similarity to another living thing either to defend itself or to get food. Natural camouflage means the animal's colouring looks very like its normal home. Snakes often have markings which blend in with the grasses and sand. Stick insects look like twigs until they begin to move.

Man has copied nature's trick of camouflage. Soldiers paint their trucks and tanks with splashes of brown and green paint so that planes flying over will mistake them for bushes.

The stick insect (1) uses its normal shape and colouring to conceal itself from predators; this is known as cryptic coloration. When disturbed, it stays motionless and resembles a twig. Soldiers, like these American GIs combing the undergrowth in Vietnam, wear special camouflage uniforms (2) to hide from the enemy. A moth (3) can appear to merge into its surroundings because of its disruptive colouration. Its muted, mottled colours seem to break up the shape of its body to an observer.

The egret's long legs are well adapted for wading, whereas the wombat can burrow and eat roots with its sharp nails and teeth. The mammoth became extinct because it could *not* adapt to the ice age conditions.

Adaptation

All living things need certain conditions to survive and each species, or different kind of plant or creature, is better suited to some conditions than to others. Water-lilies are well adapted to living with their roots in very wet conditions but most gum trees, for example, are not and will die if their roots are too wet.

Most snakes, for example, operate better in warm or hot climates because they cannot make their own body warmth as we can. In a cold climate, snakes cannot move quickly enough to catch their prey. It is for this reason that snakes generally hibernate in winter in southern Australia. Hibernation is a kind of sleep, during which the animal lives on food stored in its body fat and does not move about. Hibernation is one way in which snakes have adapted to winter.

Plants and animals have obtained their form and habits by *evolution* or development over a very long time. It is believed that the species we know in the world today have survived over many generations because they were able to adapt to their particular conditions. However, species, or certain members of species, which were not suited to a particular set of conditions, were not able to adapt quickly to their environment and so died out. That interesting fish, the Queensland mud-skipper, has been able to survive out of water on the mudflats of tidal rivers, but most fish would soon die out of the water.

The reason why some of the earliest animals have become extinct is not certain. It is suggested that they

Egret

Mammoth

Wombat

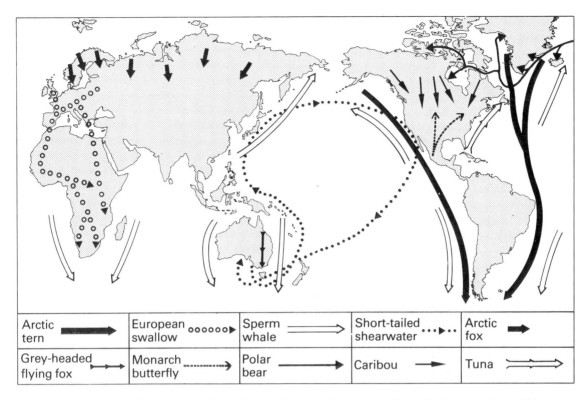

Arctic tern	European swallow ∘∘∘∘∘▸	Sperm whale ⟶	Short-tailed shearwater ⋯▸⋯	Arctic fox ➤
Grey-headed flying fox →	Monarch butterfly ⤍	Polar bear ⟶	Caribou ⟶	Tuna ⇉⇉

were not able to adapt to geological or climatic changes (such as the ice age). Also many of the larger, slow-moving animals, such as the dodo bird, fell easy prey to man who had developed the means to hunt and kill them.

Migration

Migration is the name given to the regular movement of an animal species from one place to another. Many birds and animals spend summer in one region and winter in another because they would not be able to find enough food in one place all year round. For example, some swallows spend the summer months in Australia and the winter months in Asia.

Many animals also migrate to avoid unfavourable weather and food shortages. One of Africa's most plentiful game animals, the wildebeeste or gnu, begins to migrate at the start of the dry season. At the end of the dry season, the herds break up and the animals move gradually back to their former pastures. Many thousands of animals may be on the move together at these times.

Sea creatures migrate in a similar way to birds. Many whales move from their polar feeding grounds into the

Many birds, animals and fishes migrate seasonally, moving from breeding to feeding places and returning the following year. Birds, like the arctic tern, sometimes fly thousands of miles to avoid the cold winters of the northern hemisphere. Mammals, like the caribou, may move between winter and summer quarters in search of food.

warmer seas where their young are born. The Atlantic salmon migrates to swift-flowing streams to lay eggs. The young salmon then spend up to three years in the rivers before moving down to the sea. These fish will later return to the same streams where they were born, to lay their own eggs.

Animals have no maps to guide them on their travels; their movements are instinctive and seem to be triggered off by changes in their bodies along with changes in temperature and the length of the days, which tell them when winter is approaching. When they have started to move, many animals instinctively use the sun to guide them, keeping it at a certain angle to themselves during the journey, much as we would use a compass.

Hibernation

Some animals do not migrate, but go to sleep during the colder months. This is called *hibernation.* It is different from ordinary sleep because all the animal's body functions, its *metabolism*, slow down almost to a stop. Metabolism includes all the normal life processes of the body, breathing and circulation of the blood, taking in and digestion of food, and the passing out of waste products. The animal hardly moves or breathes and has no need of food because it is using up only tiny amounts of energy. Before they go into hibernation, animals usually put on extra weight in the form of fat which the body can draw on during the long sleep. Other hibernators lay in stores of food and wake up occasionally during the winter. Animals which hibernate include bats, dormice and hedgehogs. Frogs and reptiles in colder parts of the world also sleep through the winter.

This dormouse, curled up in a nest of twigs, leaves and grass, is hibernating. Several weeks before the onset of hibernation, it lays in a store of body fat, and when the temperature drops to near freezing, it goes to sleep. Its pulse rate and body temperature drop and it is deadly cold to touch. It appears to be dead and may not be roused from sleep even if handled quite roughly.

Frogs hibernate in the mud of ponds, river banks and trees. Because they are cold-blooded and react quickly to changes in temperature, they go into hibernation in autumn in cool, temperate regions of the world. During hibernation, they live off the fat stored in their bodies as a food reserve until the spring comes.

REPRODUCTION

Life cycles

The *life cycle* of a plant or animal includes all the changes that take place during its life. The life cycle of human beings and most other backboned animals is fairly simple. It begins when an egg is fertilised and ends with the death of the individual, which usually comes after the individual has grown to maturity or *adulthood* and has produced young.

Some animals, such as the frog, have more complicated life cycles. The frog exists in three quite different forms during its life: egg, tadpole and an adult frog. Insects also have a complicated life cycle made up of several very different stages. In some species, the individual may reproduce itself but each generation of young may be different from its parents. It may take several generations of different creatures to get back to the original form. Then all the individual creatures in such a sequence are seen to be parts of a single life cycle.

All living organisms reproduce, or have young, which ensures that the species does not die out. The simplest way in which an organism can reproduce is to divide into two halves, each of which grows to the same size as the original. Single-cell organisms often reproduce in this way; it is called *asexual* reproduction.

Like all frogs, the colourful blue mountain treefrog (above) undergoes a complex life cycle. Frogs lay eggs, or frogspawn (1), which absorb heat from the sun and divide (2,3,4,) until the young tadpole is formed (5). It continues to grow until it breaks out (7) and changes its form (8,9,10,11), growing into an adult frog (12).

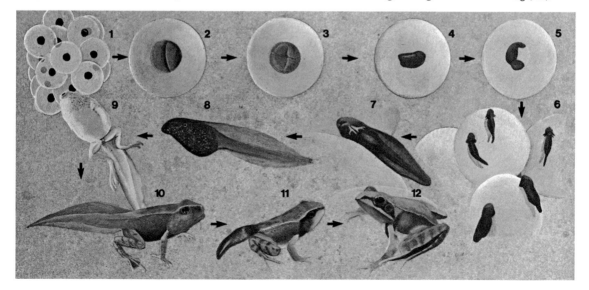

Sexual reproduction

Higher animals normally reproduce *sexually*, that is, a male cell is joined with a female cell to produce a fertilised egg which grows and develops into the new creature.

Most female fishes and *amphibians*, creatures like frogs that can live in land and water, lay eggs that are fertilised outside their bodies by males. Male birds and reptiles fertilise the egg while it is inside the female's body. Some reptiles give birth to live young as do mammals, such as humans. Mammals, with just a few exceptions, keep the young creature inside the mother's body for a certain period, called the *gestation period*, and when the young are born they are well developed.

In the sexual reproduction of all the higher animals and also of human beings, a male and a female must join together for the male to pass the male cells into the female's body to join with the egg to form a new living creature.

Both males and females have special systems of organs in their bodies which are called sex organs or *reproductive organs.* These include organs that produce

This picture sequence traces the development of the human embryo. When fertilisation takes place, the nuclei of the sperm and the egg fuse (1) and the resulting nucleus divides into two (2). Each cell divides twice (3) and further divisions (4,5) produce an inner cell mass from which the embryo (6) grows. At six weeks (7), arms and legs start to grow, and the brain grows considerably (8) at seven weeks. The embryo's limbs are well formed at eight weeks (9), and four weeks later (10), it is recognisable as being human.

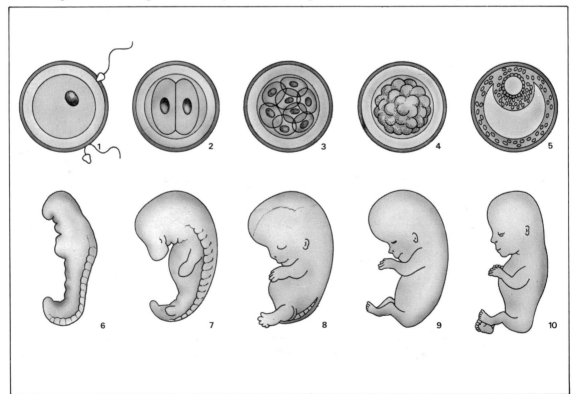

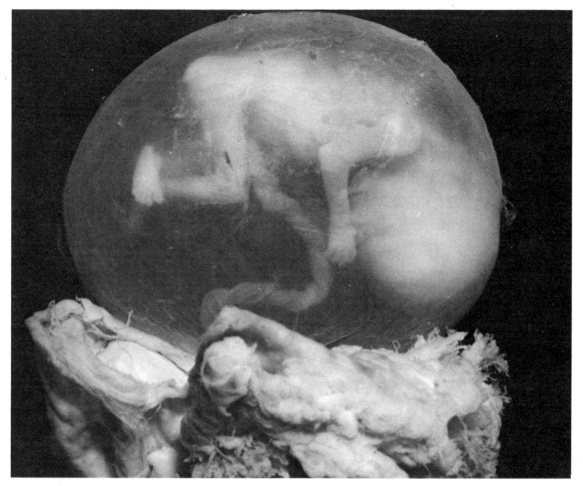

the male germ cells or *sperm* and the female egg or *ovum*. The sperm are produced in the male testicles; the ovum is produced in the female ovaries. The *penis* of the male is inserted into the *vagina* of the female, an organ which leads to the *womb*. If the male sperm unites with the ovum of the female, the new creature begins to develop in the womb and will be born at the end of the gestation period, which is different for each species. In human beings it is approximately nine months.

There are several stages involved in reproduction. Firstly; *copulation*, which is the joining of the male and female; *conception*, which is the joining of the sperm and the egg; *pregnancy*, which is the development of the new creature in the womb; and *parturition* or giving birth.

Conception can only take place when a new egg is released from the ovaries of the female, and this takes place only at certain times which are different for each species.

The shape and limbs of this human embryo inside the amnion are clearly visible. The coiled umbilical cord attaches the foetus to the womb of its mother.

MAMMALS

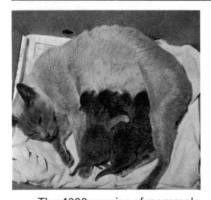

The 4000 species of mammals are divided into three groups: monotremes; marsupials; and placentals. The duckbilled platypus (top) is a monotreme, an egg-laying mammal, whereas the Burmese cat (above) is a placental, which, like Man, nourishes the embryo by means of a true internal placenta.

Mammals may be as different as a bat and a huge blue whale, but they all belong to the same group of warm-blooded animals with backbones. Their young are fed for a time on milk from the mother's own body. They all have the same kind of heart and blood and the lower jaw of a mammal is always made up of one bone on each side. This is important because the bones are often preserved as fossils and help scientists to follow the development of mammals through the centuries.

Most mammals live on land, although some such as whales and seals have adapted to life in the water, while bats have taken to the air. Because most mammals have fur coats and can keep their bodies at a constant high temperature, they are able to live in some of the coldest parts of the world.

Mammals have also a much better developed brain than other animals. They have more ability to learn and to change their behaviour to suit different situations. Young mammals are always looked after by their mothers for a time, while they learn to find food and avoid their enemies and grow strong enough to survive.

Primates

These are a group of mammals which include monkeys, apes and human beings. Most of the primates have hair, and have well developed brains and good eyesight. Their arms and legs have five fingers and toes with nails instead of claws. Apes are the nearest relatives to man. There are only nine living kinds of apes, the chimpanzee, the gorilla, the orang-utan and six species of gibbons. The apes are different from almost all of the monkeys in that they have no tails.

Monkeys and apes are primates, but unlike apes, monkeys nearly always have a tail. The orang-utan and gibbon are arboreal and extremely agile apes. The gorilla is the largest ape, whereas the intelligent chimpanzee most resembles Man. The bald-headed uakari is a New World monkey from the rain-forests of the River Amazon. It has a short tail and swings by its long arms from branch to branch. The squirrel monkey has a long, coiled prehensile tail.

Orang-utan

Gorilla

Chimpanzee

Gibbon

Uakari

Squirrel monkeys

Special groups of mammals

This family tree demonstrates the diversity of rodents, which range in size from the tiny house mouse to the large South American capybara, which resembles a giant guinea pig. The largest order of mammals, rodents are found in every continent except Antarctica.

There are many large groups of mammals. One of these is the *rodents*, which include the rat and the mouse, the squirrels, beavers and porcupines. There are over two thousand different kinds of rodents, nearly as many as all the other kinds of mammals put together. The rodents all have two pairs of sharp chisel-like teeth at the front of the mouth, which they use to gnaw food, dig burrows and

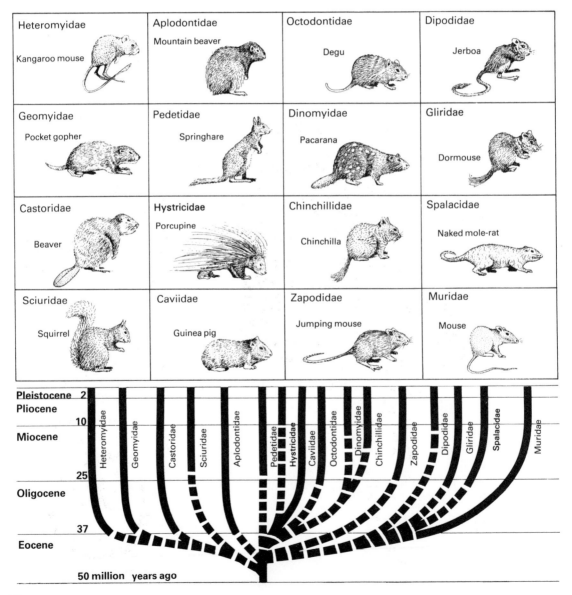

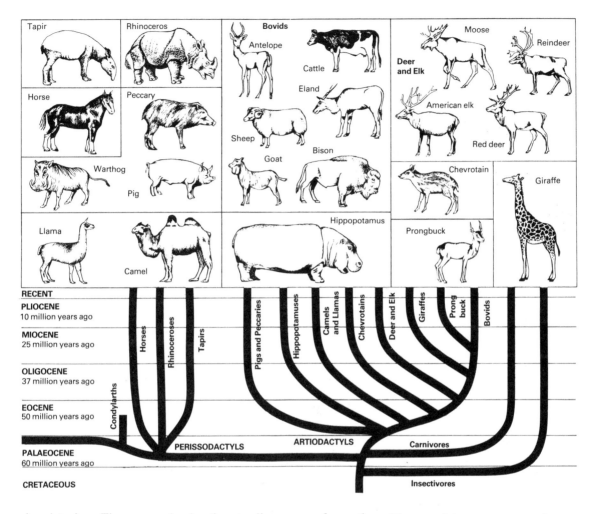

RECENT											
PLIOCENE 10 million years ago											
MIOCENE 25 million years ago		Horses	Rhinoceroses	Tapirs	Pigs and Peccaries	Hippopotamuses	Camels and Llamas	Chevrotains	Deer and Elk	Giraffes	Prong buck	Bovids
OLIGOCENE 37 million years ago											
EOCENE 50 million years ago	Condylarths										
			PERISSODACTYLS		ARTIODACTYLS			Carnivores			
PALAEOCENE 60 million years ago											
CRETACEOUS						Insectivores					

shred twigs. The name 'rodent' actually comes from the Latin word 'roders' which means to gnaw.

The gnawing teeth in front have a gap separating them from the rest of the teeth. By pulling the lip into this gap when gnawing, the rodent can stop wood and other things from entering its mouth.

Some rodents are valuable to man while others do much damage. Rats and mice destroy a lot of food and crops. Rats also damage buildings. On the other hand, many rodents such as beavers and chinchillas provide valuable fur. The Incas of Peru reared guinea pigs for their meat. Today we keep them as pets. They are also used in laboratories to test drugs.

Two other most important groups of mammals are the *ungulates*, which include cows, sheep and camels and most of the grass-eaters, and the *cetaceans* — water-living mammals such as whales and dolphins.

The ungulates are a group of hooved animals that walk on the tips of their toes. They are divided into two groups: artiodactyls, or even-toed ungulates; and perissodactyls, or odd-toed ungulates. There are only three perissodactyl families but the artiodactyls, which include cattle, deer, antelopes and pigs, are a large group of eight families in total.

Flying mammals

Bats are the only mammals which can really fly. Their wings are made of folds of skin joined to the sides of the body. Bats are all *nocturnal,* or night animals, but their eyes are not good so they rely on a kind of radar to find their way about. To do this they send out a stream of high pitched sounds and pick up the echoes when they bounce back from nearby objects. This helps them to avoid flying into walls and trees and to detect flying insects so they can catch them in the air.

As well as the insect eaters, there are fruit bats which have wingspans more than 50cm across. They feed on soft fruits and nectar. The vampire bats feed entirely on the blood of birds and animals and sometimes man.

These flying foxes roost in trees during the day, hanging free from the high branches, and fly off in search of food at dusk. Their diet consists of fruit, nectar and pollen.

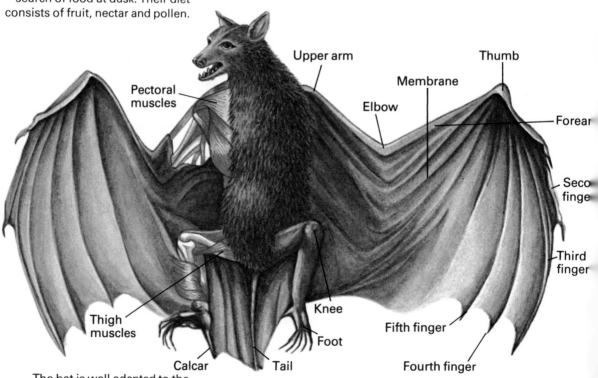

The bat is well adapted to the requirements of flight. It has a light skeleton with powerful forelimbs and strong shoulder joints.

Above: This wallaby, with a baby joey in its pouch, is a marsupial. When the hairless, blind young animal is born, it bursts out of the fluid filled amnion and climbs through the mother's fur to the pouch where it attaches itself to a teat. It receives no help from its mother and is probably guided by its sense of smell.

Above left: The echidna, or spiny anteater as it is often called, is an egg-laying mammal. The egg is incubated in the female's pouch, and when the newborn animal breaks out of the egg, it attaches itself to the teats in the pouch.

Monotremes and Marsupials

Monotremes are the most primitive mammals, for they still lay eggs. They have not developed or evolved so far as other mammals. They have hair and feed their young with their own milk. The most famous is the platypus and another is the spiny anteater which lays one egg at a time.

Marsupials are mammals which carry their young in pouches, such as the kangaroo, the koala and the possum. Young marsupials are not developed enough to live on their own when they are born and must continue to grow for some time in their mother's pouch. The baby kangaroo is only about 2.5 cm long when it is born although its mother may stand more than 1.5m tall. Even though it is so tiny, this small kangaroo still manages to struggle through the jungle of its mother's fur to find its way into her pouch where it feeds on her milk for the next few months. The baby, or joey, leaves the pouch when it is about nine months old but returns to feed until it is about fifteen months old.

Reptiles are vertebrates, animals with backbones, and their bodies are covered with horny scales. They are called *cold-blooded* animals, which means that their body temperature always remains about the same as their surroundings, which is why lizards and some snakes love to lie in the warm sun.

They are basically air-breathing animals with well developed lungs, although a few reptiles like the aquatic turtles can use the oxygen in water and can stay underwater for several days. Nearly all reptiles lay eggs. Reptiles include alligators, crocodiles, lizards, snakes and tortoises.

This cut-away illustration of a crocodile shows its skeleton and internal organs. Its heart, like that of the alligator and caiman, has two ventricles and two auricles but the venous and arterial blood are mixed. The Crocodylia order first appeared in the Triassic era and the crocodile is a direct decendant of early reptiles.

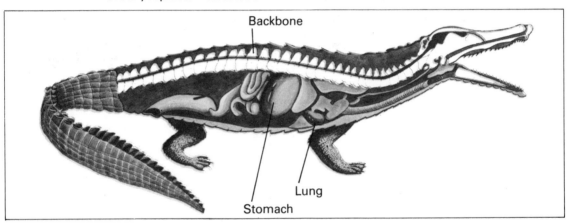

Backbone

Lung

Stomach

Ancient reptiles

The first reptiles occurred on the earth nearly 300 million years ago when large areas of land were covered with swampy forests. Many amphibians which looked like large salamanders roamed these forests and some of these evolved into reptiles. Among the changes which allowed

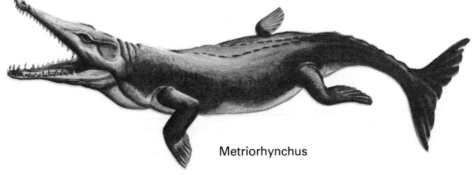

Metriorhynchus

the reptiles to live away from the water was the development of a skin which protected the animal from drying out when it was not in the water, and eggs with skins which protected them from dehydration. Without these two developments reptiles would have had to live near water. As the swamps dried up and more land appeared, the reptiles spread out rapidly, dividing into two groups. One group would later develop into mammals while the other branch evolved into most of the reptiles we know today. These developments took millions of years. Some of the most famous reptiles of these early periods were the huge *tyrannosaurus* and the flying *pterodactyls.*

The ancient reptiles, known as dinosaurs, were enormous and included the largest animals that have ever lived. Most dinosaurs became extinct in the Cretaceous era 70,000,000 years ago when the earth's crust was undergoing great upheavals. However, the tuatara, which lives off the coast of New Zealand, is a relic from the Triassic age of reptiles.

Proganochelys

Tuatara

Pleisiosaur

Tyrannosaurus

Stegosaurus

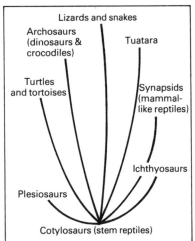

Top: This spiny, soft shelled turtle is a large reptile that lives in fresh water. Its leathery soft shell lacks horny plates.

Above: This family tree shows that reptiles evolved from the early primitive amphibians.

The family tree labels:
Lizards and snakes
Archosaurs (dinosaurs & crocodiles)
Tuatara
Turtles and tortoises
Synapsids (mammal-like reptiles)
Ichthyosaurs
Plesiosaurs
Cotylosaurs (stem reptiles)

Kinds of reptiles

About a hundred million years ago, the numbers of different reptiles began to decline until most of them disappeared. Only four small groups remain today.

The first group includes turtles and tortoises; the second covers crocodiles and alligators; the third includes lizards and snakes, and the fourth group has only one member still living, this is the *tuatara* which lives on a few small islands off the coast of New Zealand. Although it looks very like a lizard, the tuatara is quite different and its distant relatives go back in history even further than the dinosaurs so scientists have called it a 'living fossil'.

Reptiles today are much smaller than their ancient ancestors, although some crocodiles reach over 5m long and some snakes may reach 10m in length. Reptiles enjoy living in warm climates and the largest reptiles are found in the hottest places. This is because the only heat they have in their bodies is absorbed from their surroundings. A large reptile could not absorb enough heat to keep active in cooler areas. In cool climates, some smaller lizards and snakes go into hibernation for the winter.

Reptiles also have very small brains, usually less than 1 per cent of their total body weight. Their brains are less well developed than the brains of mammals.

Snakes and lizards

There are more than 5500 different kinds of snakes and lizards; they are the most successful living reptiles. They live everywhere from the sea to the driest deserts and different species have adapted for running, climbing, swimming and burrowing. The only places snakes are not found are the Polar regions, which are too cold, Ireland and New Zealand, and some other small islands. Snakes can vary in size from creatures no bigger than a pencil up to the huge anaconda which can grow to over 10 m.

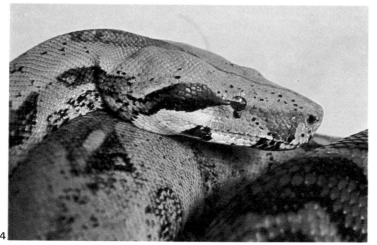

The crocodile *C. johnstoni* (1), from Australia, is 2.5 m long with a slender snout and a wide mouth filled with sharp teeth. The tuatara (2), a relic from Triassic times, is found on 20 islands off the coast of New Zealand. This 'living fossil' has a lizard-like appearance and belongs to the otherwise extinct order of Rhynchocephalia. The monitor (3) is a snake-like lizard with a slender body and forked tongue. The carpet python (4) may lay from 8-100 eggs about three months after mating.

Caecilians, salamanders and newts are all amphibians. The caecilian belongs to the Apoda order of legless and burrowing amphibians, whereas newts and salamanders both belong to the Caudata order of amphibians with tails. Newts are terrestrial for most of the year and became aquatic in the breeding season. Salamanders may be terrestrial, aquatic, semi-aquatic or arboreal.

The snake's long, slender body has more ribs and vertebrae than any other backboned animal, so they are much more flexible and can curl their bodies into tight coils. Snakes have no eardrums but listen by picking up vibrations from the ground, which is why so few snakes are seen in the bush. They pick up the vibrations caused by footsteps and slither away. All snakes are meat eaters and nearly always eat living food. To find their prey they use mostly sight and scent, although snakes detect scents in a different way to humans. The forked tongue which is always flicking in and out is actually smelling the air and carrying traces of scent back to a special organ — the Jacobson's organ — which a snake has in the roof of its mouth.

Amphibians

The word *amphibian* means 'double life' and creatures which are amphibious live two kinds of life: the first part in the water and the later part mostly on land.

The amphibians are a very ancient group of backboned animals which were first on earth about 400 million years ago, when the first fishes found they could learn to breathe air and move about on land. The first amphibians were clumsy and awkward moving on dry land and still needed to be close to the water.

Some of the first amphibians developed into reptiles and lived completely on the land, while some types disappeared altogether. A few remained, however, and their descendants are the frogs, salamanders and other amphibians of today. Even today, most of these creatures still need to be close to the water, for their skins cannot protect their bodies from losing moisture in dry air, so they must stay in damp places to stay alive. Most

Caecilian

Newt

Salamander

amphibians start life as tadpoles and they must always return to the water to breed

Amphibians are divided into three main groups. The first are called *apodans.* They are mostly burrowing animals which live in tropical climates. They have no legs and have only very small eyes because they have adapted to living under the ground. One type lives in the water but most burrow in damp soil.

The second group are the *urodeles,* also called salamander and newts. They are more like the very first amphibians than any of the others. Although most are small, one kind of salamander – the giant salamander of Japan — grows to over 1.5m in length. They lay their eggs on water plants and the eggs hatch into tadpoles. The tadpoles start life breathing through gills, but gradually they grow legs and lungs and turn into adult salamanders. Several types of salamanders have adapted so well to living on land that they do not have to go back to the water to breed. Instead, the mother lays big watery eggs and the tadpoles develop in this miniature tank until they are ready to hatch as salamanders. Other salamanders keep the eggs inside their bodies while the tadpoles are developing, so that the young are born alive.

The third group of amphibians are the *anurans,* which are frogs and toads. Frogs have smooth skins and the toads usually have warty skins. Frogs have especially well developed hind legs for jumping. They vary from a tiny tree frog less than 2.5 cm long to the huge goliath frog from Africa which grows up to almost a metre long.

Most anurans lay their eggs in the water. The eggs are in jelly-like masses or strings called spawn, which produce the tadpoles. If you live near a dam or a pond, you have probably heard the loud croaking of the frogs and toads during their spring courtship. If you fill a container with water from the pond and place some frog spawn into it (a piece about the size of a tennis ball is enough) you can watch the tadpoles develop and gradually change into fully formed frogs. The young tadpoles feed on tiny plants in the water. As they develop, small amounts of fresh pond water and small amounts of fish food can be added.

Like the salamanders, the anurans include some species which live completely on land and some which live wholly in the water. They breathe through their skins and the adult frogs and toads feed by snapping up small creatures with their jaws. Land-living frogs and toads have long sticky tongues which they shoot out to catch small insects. Anurans are found in most parts of the world, even as far north as the Arctic Circle.

Tree frog

Marsupial frog

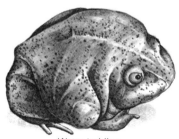

Water-holding frog

The tree frog is characterised by fleshy discs on the ends of its fingers and toes. The female marsupial frog carries its eggs in a pouch on its back. The water-holding frog of Australia can store water in its bladder and so survive long drought periods.

The birds

Birds are warm-blooded animals whose bodies are covered with feathers. They range in size from the tiny humming birds less than 5 cm long to the ostrich which grows to over 2 m tall.

The birds were probably the last large group of animals to appear on the earth. We do not know when the first bird appeared but we do know that it grew and evolved from some sort of reptile, probably from a group of reptiles which had taken to living in the trees. Although the *pterodactyl* could fly, it was such a different kind of creature from the true birds that we know that birds did not evolve from it.

Remains of the earliest birds have been found in Germany. These fossils show creatures that had teeth and long tails like reptiles, but their feathers were well formed and they were clearly birds.

Birds have no teeth. Instead they have tough, horny beaks. The kind of food the bird eats depends on the shape of the bill. Seed-eating birds have stout beaks which can crack the seeds while meat-eating birds have strong, hooked beaks which they use to tear the meat.

There are about 9000 different kinds of birds on earth and most can fly. But a few, such as the emu and the

Right: This cut-away picture of a bird shows that the bones are fused to provide a rigid fulcrum for the wing action in flight. The skeleton is very light, the bones being hollow. The bird's breast muscles are powerful and well developed to supply motive power when flying, and the body itself is streamlined and has an aerodynamic shape for flying.

Far right: The penguin is a large flightless bird, which lives on the icy shores of Antarctica. The small wings are used as flippers when swimming underwater. Although the wing bones are short and flat, they are similar in structure to those of a flying bird.

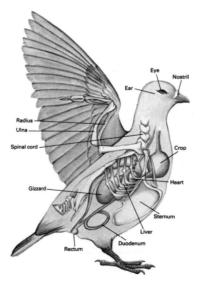

ostrich, have lost the ability to fly and they have no large flight muscles. Penguins do not fly. Their wings are adapted to swimming in the sea and are rather like flippers.

How birds fly

Any flying object or creature must use two forces. It must have *lift* to keep it up in the air and it must have *thrust* to push it along. The wings of birds are beautifully constructed to provide both lift and thrust. The feathers produce a curved surface and the air passing over this surface is 'stretched out' in comparison with the air passing underneath the wing. This reduces the pressure on top of the wing and allows the stronger pressure under the wing to lift the bird.

Next time you watch a bird in flight, see how it glides and soars almost effortlessly on the air currents. The albatross, for example, skims backwards and forwards over the water and hardly ever flaps its wings. The wings are very long and narrow and ideal for gliding on the strong winds over the oceans.

The large birds of prey or hunting birds, like hawks and eagles, soar by letting rising currents of air take them upwards. They move slowly but get enough lift because their wings are very broad.

Most birds fly by flapping their wings. They make their own thrust by twisting the wing-tips with each flap. This twisting movement pushes back on the air around them and so drives the bird forwards. Birds need large muscles to move the wings up and down and these are attached to a broad keel which sticks out of the breast bone and looks very much like the keel of a yacht.

The large emu is a flightless Australian bird. Its tiny wings are only one-tenth of its body length. During the dry seasons, it migrates over long distances in search of water.

Most birds build nests in which they incubate their eggs and rear their young. This nest contains a young seagull chick.

Nesting

All birds lay eggs and most make a neat nest in which to lay them. This can be just a hollow in the ground, or it can be beautifully woven out of grass, twigs and other materials. When the eggs have been laid, they must be kept warm and almost all birds sit on their eggs to warm them. Some, such as the brush turkey, may pile leaves and twigs over their eggs to keep them warm.

Most birds are quite helpless when they are born. They have to be fed and kept warm by their parents for a few weeks until their feathers have grown and they can leave

This flight sequence shows the flapping motion of a duck. When the wings flap, the tips move faster than the rest of the wings, providing the thrust for sustained flight. The bird's streamlined shape and lightweight skeleton are perfectly adapted for flight.

the nest. Many of the young of ground and water-nesting birds are much stronger and can run around and look after themselves as soon as they hatch out of the egg, although they usually stay with their mother for some time.

Fishes

Fishes are cold-blooded animals with backbones. Their bodies are usually covered with scales. They live in water and breathe by taking oxygen from the water using organs called gills at the sides of their throats. The fish takes water in through its mouth and the water is forced out through the gills. Oxygen from the water enters the fish's bloodstream from the gills and the water passes out through the slits of the gills.

The earliest fishes came into being about 500 million years ago. From fossils in rocks we know they were small with no jaws and bony skins. In fact they are called *ostracoderms,* which means 'bony skins'. Most of them died out as new kinds of fishes developed, but some, like the lampreys and the hagfishes, strange eel-like creatures, are survivors from the early fishes.

This cross-section through a fish shows the skeleton and internal organs. Although there are many variations in body shape and the position and number of fins, the basic structure is similar to that of most vertebrates. Most of the body is muscular tissue and the skeleton protects the fish's vital organs.

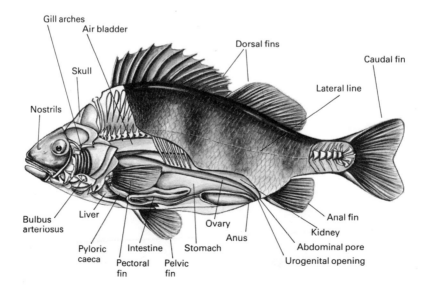

Gill arches
Air bladder
Skull
Dorsal fins
Caudal fin
Lateral line
Nostrils
Bulbus arteriosus
Liver
Pyloric caeca
Pectoral fin
Intestine
Pelvic fin
Stomach
Ovary
Anus
Anal fin
Kidney
Abdominal pore
Urogenital opening

How fishes swim

Fishes swim by moving their bodies from side to side. This produces a backward thrust on the water and pushes the body forward. Most fish have fins which help them keep their balance and change direction.

Fishes can hear, see and smell. As well, they have a special organ with which they can sense movement and water pressure. This organ is called the *lateral line* because it is a kind of groove or tube along the fish's body.

The bony fishes

Most fishes have skeletons of bone and their scales are usually thin and overlap each other. Very early in their history, the bony fishes developed into two groups which evolved in different ways. One group, called the lobe-finned fishes, had thick fins like limbs. They later evolved into the amphibians and only a few species still exist today. These are the *coelacanths* and the lungfishes. Scientists thought the coelacanths had died out millions of years ago until some were caught in the Indian Ocean.

Another big group is called ray-finned. They have delicate fins with thin bones called rays. These fishes range from slender mackerel to the eel, the seahorse and the various flatfishes such as the plaice and the sole.

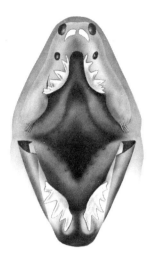

The jaws of this Australian lungfish, *Neoceratodus forsteri*, have large nostrils and bony toothplates. This primitive fish, which dates back to the Devonian and Triassic periods, is found only in a few rivers in northern Queensland. It has one lung and large bony scales.

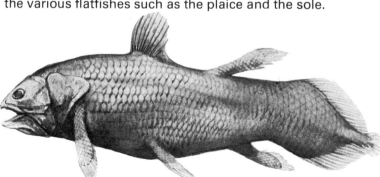

Sharks and rays

Sharks and rays have no true bones in their bodies. Their skeletons are made of hard tissue called cartilage and their bodies are very rough and covered with pointed scales. These scales go all the way to their mouths where

Coelacanths were long believed extinct, but since 1938 about 40 have been discovered off the coast of Madagascar. They appeared 400,000,000 years ago in the Devonian period. They have extremely small brains and a hinged bony skull.

The stingray has a flat body and large wing-like pectoral fins. At the base of its tail is a sharp spine, or sting, which it uses as a means of defence to inflict a painful wound. Its speckled body camouflages it well against the pebbles on the sea floor.

they extend to form several rows of sharp teeth. The largest of all fishes is the whale shark which grows up to 18m long.

The rays have one pair of fins which have become much bigger than the rest. You can see these rays sometimes breaking the surface of the water as they glide along on their huge wing-like fins.

Flying fishes

The large pectoral fins of flying fishes are specially adapted for gliding above water and can spread like wings. Flying fishes may reach speeds of up to 56 kph, and it is thought that they make use of the updraughts of air in the troughs of waves.

Flying fishes are fairly small and have long fins like wings which often take up half the length of their bodies. They live in large groups or shoals close to the surface of the water, mainly in warm seas, usually far away from land. They fly by using their large fins to glide over the surface from time to time. They use their large tail fin to drive themselves quickly to the surface of the water, break through and keep on going for a short way through the air before coming back to the water.

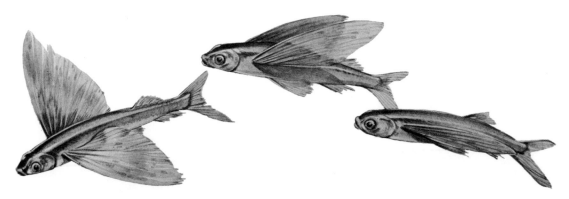

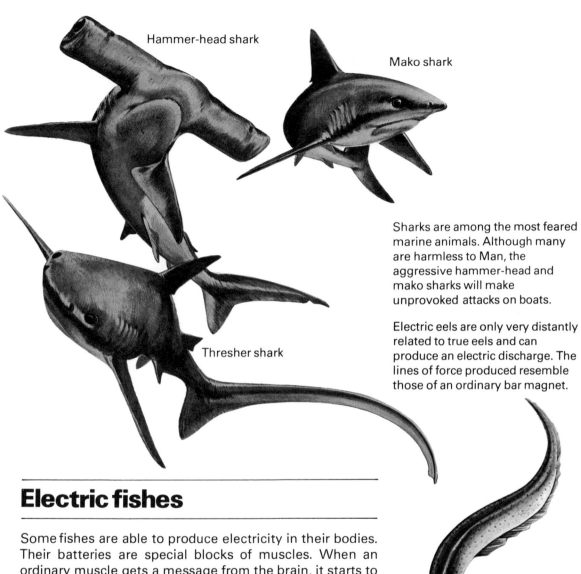

Hammer-head shark

Mako shark

Thresher shark

Sharks are among the most feared marine animals. Although many are harmless to Man, the aggressive hammer-head and mako sharks will make unprovoked attacks on boats.

Electric eels are only very distantly related to true eels and can produce an electric discharge. The lines of force produced resemble those of an ordinary bar magnet.

Electric eel

Electric fishes

Some fishes are able to produce electricity in their bodies. Their batteries are special blocks of muscles. When an ordinary muscle gets a message from the brain, it starts to move. Electric fish have special muscles which cannot move, but instead when they receive a message from the brain – really a very small electric current – they give out electricity. If they use all these muscles at the same time, a powerful shock can be felt in the water nearby. Among the best-known electric fishes are the electric eel, the electric catfish and the electric ray. The electric eel can kill fish for eating by producing powerful bursts of electricity, up to 550 volts – strong enough to stun a horse straying in the same water. Other electric fish use electric discharges to defend themselves or to help them find their way about in muddy water.

INSECTS AND SPIDERS

Insects

Like most arthropods, insects have a segmented body and external skeleton. The view of a typical insect (below) and the cut-away drawing (below right) show the fused segments that form its head, thorax and abdomen.

Insects belong to a large group of the animal kingdom called the *arthropods.* They are related to crabs and spiders. You can recognise adult insects because they always have a body divided into three parts; the head, the *thorax* or trunk, and the *abdomen* or hind part. They also have three pairs of legs. Insects also have a pair of feelers or *antennae* and many also have two pairs of wings. Because they have no backbones, insects are invertebrates, the only invertebrates with wings. Many have no wings, such as the fleas and lice that live among the fur or feathers of warm-blooded animals.

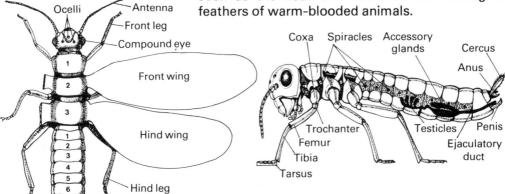

THORAX { 1 Prothorax
2 Mesothorax
3 Metathorax

ABDOMEN 1-11

How insects breathe

Although there are more than three-quarters of a million different kinds of insects and probably many more still to be discovered, they never grow very large. This is because of their way of breathing. Insects breathe through many small tubes called *trachea.* These tubes are connected to the outside air by small openings. Through these openings air enters and spreads along the breathing tubes to all parts of the body, a slow system which could not provide the insect with enough oxygen if its body were larger. They also have a non-bony outer skeleton which could not support a larger body.

The largest insect is the African goliath beetle, which grows as large as a man's fist. Some butterflies and moths have wingspans of several centimetres. Some of the largest insects are the silk moths, whose larvae spin cocoons from which we make silk.

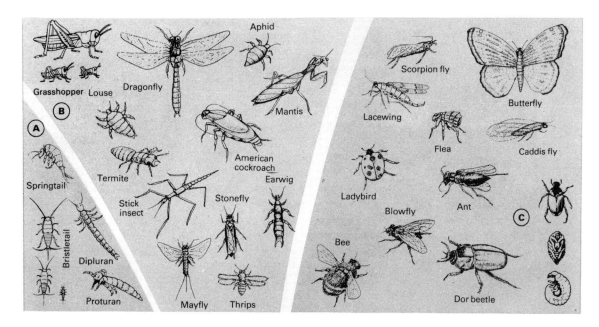

Aphid
Grasshopper Louse Dragonfly Mantis
B
A Scorpion fly
Lacewing Butterfly
Springtail Termite American cockroach Earwig Flea Caddis fly
Bristletail Stick insect Stonefly Ladybird
Dipluran Blowfly Ant C
Bee
Proturan Mayfly Thrips Dor beetle

Life cycles

As they grow, insects go through several stages in their life, in which they look like completely different creatures. These changes are called the insect's *metamorphosis,* or transformation.

Insects fall into two main groups according to how they change during their lives. The first group changes very little; grasshoppers are an example. Soon after it has left the egg, the young insect looks like a miniature adult except that it has no wings. It is called a *nymph.* Like all other insects, the nymph has to change its skin regularly or *moult.* After each moult, the wings grow larger until the insect is fully grown.

The other group changes completely from its young stage to the adult form. The young insect which comes out of its egg is called a *larva* or caterpillar. It changes its skin too, but after each moult it simply becomes larger. After a certain number of moults, it spins a silky web around itself called a *cocoon*, changes its skin again, and becomes a stiff, immobile *pupa* or *chrysalis.* Inside, a great change takes place; nature rebuilds the larva into its adult form, which can take a few days or many months depending on the kind of insect it is. At last, the adult emerges. If it has wings, these will be crumpled and soft but soon they will dry out and become strong enough for the insect to fly. Butterflies and bees have this sort of life history.

This insect family tree shows their division into three basic groups. Group A includes the primitive wingless insects that do not undergo a process of metamorphosis. Group B contains those insects with incomplete or gradual metamorphosis. The insects in Group C undergo complete metamorphosis.

Insects and man

Some insects are valuable to man. Some provide a valuable service by carrying pollen from flower to flower so new flowers will grow. Bees provide us with honey. The ladybird beetle helps to control plant lice and other pests.

Some insects are harmful to man, such as termites which feed on wood and do great harm to buildings. Many blood-feeding insects attack men and animals and also carry disease. The mosquito and the tsetse fly carry the micro-organisms that cause malaria and sleeping sickness. One of the most dangerous insects is the common housefly, found nearly all over the world. Flies like dung and decaying matter and carry many bacteria which cause diseases such as typhoid fever, cholera and dysentery.

Spiders

Spiders are not insects, but with scorpions, mites and ticks they make up the *arachnids.* Their bodies are divided into two sections, the head and the abdomen, and they have four pairs of legs. They feel and smell their way about using two organs called *palps,* near their mouths. All spiders feed on other creatures, usually insects which they catch in traps or webs. These webs are made of fine sticky silk which the spider spins from its own body.

Some spiders are dangerous because of their poisonous bites and scorpions are feared for their stings. Mites and ticks are pests because many of them suck the blood of higher animals, like cattle, dogs and man. Ticks can cause paralysis with the poison that flows from their bodies into the body of the creature they feed on.

Dangerous spiders include the black widow of North America and the funnel-web and redback of Australia. Their bites can kill human beings.

The butterfly undergoes a full metamorphosis in its development from egg to fully-grown adult. The caterpillar, which hatches from the egg, spins a cocoon in which it becomes a pupa. The adult emerges from the hard-cased pupa when fully grown.

The trapdoor spider (1) spins a silk-lined shaft and a hinged door at the entrance to its burrow. The funnel-web spider (2) builds a silken, tubular funnel.

ANIMALS AND MAN

Conservation

Animals, minerals and plants are all part of earth's resources, the environment that help us to live. Because human beings are increasing in numbers and are also increasing their needs, they are using up earth's resources and destroying the environment very quickly. The way to use resources sensibly for the good of mankind is called *conservation.* This means 'protection from loss or waste' and it is just as important to conserve animals as forests, gold or anything else.

Every animal has an important part to play in nature and is needed in the life of some other animal, as we see in food chains. When a species of animal becomes *extinct* or dies out, many other living things are affected.

National parks are places where animals can be conserved in all their beauty and variety. Many such parks now exist in the United States of America, Australia, Africa and many other countries. In many parks and zoos, rare animals are being bred and in some cases, returned to the wild. Some animals are protected by law from hunting, but this is not always enough.

This elephant is protected from indiscriminate hunters and poachers in the Kruger National Park, South Africa. Game reserves and national parks play an important role in the conservation of threatened species. They protect wildlife from man and preserve the natural environment of the animals.

Breeding

Early man obtained all his food by hunting animals, but it was not until recent centuries that man has tried to produce animals to suit himself. This is known as *breeding.* All of our farm animals and pets today are the descendants of wild species. Man first made friends with wild dogs around ten thousand years ago. These dogs developed into all the kinds of dogs we know today, mainly because man controlled their breeding.

Breeding animals involves using the best male and female of a species to produce very good quality offspring. Two animals with different good points may be bred to produce a young animal which has all the good points combined. An example of how breeding changes animals little by little is seen in the difference between wild pigs and farm pigs. Most wild pigs are heavier in front than they are at the back, but the best meat comes from the back parts. So farmers bred only pigs which had large hindquarters until at last all their pigs were heavier at the back.

Animal products

Many animals supply man with food. Poultry are bred for their meat or eggs, pork and bacon come from pigs, mutton and lamb from sheep and steak from specially bred cattle.

Many of the materials used to make clothes come from animals. The best example is wool, the natural crinkled hair of sheep. The wool is stretchy and the crinkles in the fibre help to trap air, making woollen garments very warm. Silk is another important animal fibre which can be made into soft, shiny fabrics. Silk is produced in a long unbroken thread, often a kilometre long; it is actually fibre that silkworms use to make their cocoons.

One of the finest quality fibres, which is also called wool, comes from the alpaca, a relative of the camel found in South America. Other animals which supply us with natural fibres are the goats of Kashmir and Tibet, from which we get soft cashmere wool to make sweaters, the angora goat which produces mohair, and the vicuna, a camel-like animal.

This woman is spinning wool by means of a traditional spinning wheel. Sheep's wool is an important animal product, which is used for clothing, blankets, floor coverings, soft furnishings and rugs.

Veterinary doctors have to treat a wide range of animals, including household pets, zoo and farm animals. The vets (1) are performing an emergency operation on a horse in a special surgical unit. However, most vets have to work 'on the job' like the vet (2) who is operating on a cow in the outbuildings of a farm. The little dog (3) has had its broken leg set in plaster at a special hospital for dogs.

Veterinary medicine

Veterinary doctors, often called vets or animal doctors, treat animals which are sick. They do a wide variety of work from setting a dog's broken leg to extracting decayed teeth from a gorilla.

Many veterinarians look after pets when they are ill or injured in accidents. They are also called upon by farmers who need help with their cattle and other farm animals.

Veterinarians have to be very highly trained. Some work in research, trying to discover better ways to feed animals, or to cure sick animals. Others give advice to farmers on which farm animals are best for certain areas, and what animal feeds are best. Veterinarians also work very closely with doctors because some animal diseases can be caught by humans.

INDEX

Page numbers in italics refer to an illustration on that page.
Bold type refers to a heading or sub-heading.